PHYSICS

Colin Maunder

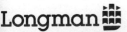

Longman Group UK Limited,
Longman House, Burnt Mill, Harlow,
Essex CM20 2JE, England
and Associated Companies throughout the world.

First published 1988
Reprinted 1988

ISBN 0582 02983 X

Set in 9½/11 Century Schoolbook
Printed in Great Britain
by Richard Clay plc, Bungay, Suffolk

Series Editors: Geoff Black and Stuart Wall

Titles available in the Longman Pass Pack series

Biology	French
Business Studies	Geography
Chemistry	Home Economics: Food
English	Mathematics
English Literature	Physics

ACKNOWLEDGEMENTS

The author is indebted to the following Examination Groups for permission to reproduce past examination questions. Whilst permission has been granted to reproduce their questions, the answers or hints on answers are solely the responsibility of the author and have not been provided or approved by the Group.

London and East Anglian Group (LEAG).

Northern Examining Association (NEA), incorporating the Associated Lancashire, Joint Matriculation, North Regional, North West Regional, and Yorkshire and Humberside Regional Examination Boards.

Northern Ireland Schools Examination Council (NISEC).

INTRODUCTION

This booklet is arranged in the order of the thirteen units presented on the audio-tape, and gives you extra information and advice on each topic area. It uses charts, diagrams and tables to give you helpful summaries, and provides extra questions and answers on each topic area.

You can also see how the examiner assesses the work of candidates. The tape and booklet can be used on their own but are best used together,

first by listening to a unit on the tape, then by reading the booklet on that unit.

GCSE PHYSICS

It will be helpful if you can obtain a copy of your particular examination syllabus, because there are variations between the examination boards in the depth of study of topics. However the GCSE exams follow guidelines called 'National Criteria' so that whatever syllabus you are following, the same basic topics will be covered.

The GCSE exam is designed to test what you **can** do, not to trip you up or set 'catch questions', so you should approach it with confidence. You may already have your course assessment marks and these will count towards your final grade, but practice in exam technique is helpful and can improve on your grade.

The exam papers will reflect some of the skills you should have acquired, and the questions are designed to test these skills.

QUESTION TYPES

MULTIPLE CHOICE QUESTIONS

These require an A-E response and are there to see if you have basic facts at your fingertips. The tape and this booklet should help you check these facts. Where you are in doubt you should check your own notes and your school or college textbooks.

STRUCTURED QUESTIONS

These require a sequence of short answers, usually a line or two of writing. The questions increase in difficulty, but if you find you cannot answer a part of a question don't be discouraged; look at all the parts and answer what you can. The important thing is to write a whole sentence answer, and to explain clearly any decisions you have made.

Some of the questions will rely on *mathematical* answers. Remember to write down *all* the steps you make, explaining what you have done. Don't simply rely on your calculator.

Let the examiner see the stages of your calculation, and remember that a physical quantity has *units* like kg, m/s and so on!

UNSTRUCTURED QUESTIONS

These are usually longer and require more of you. You need to plan your answer to ensure that you are giving all the necessary detail. You will find the outline answers in this booklet helpful in giving you a model on which to base your own work.

To summarise, the exam will test your *knowledge* – your ability to recall facts and information. It will also test your *understanding*, i.e. your ability to apply information to a situation, to draw conclusions from data and to apply your skills to a practical situation.

EXAMINATION AND REVISION TECHNIQUES

First, make sure you know what *topics* you have covered. List them and decide which topics you understand well, and which need practice. Physics is a logical subject and a weakness in one area can cause problems in another. The topics have been arranged on the tape and in this booklet to begin with basic ideas and to deal with ideas of roughly increasing difficulty, so this could act as a guide.

MAKING A SUMMARY

For each topic, make a *summary*. Simply writing a sequence of headings will help you organise your thoughts on a topic. A summary might contain some or all of the following:

1 definitions (e.g. what does acceleration mean?)
2 a list of the units of measurement (e.g. m/s^2)
3 some notes about ideas (difference between velocity and acceleration; uniform and non-uniform acceleration)
4 detail about important experiments (e.g. to show that force is proportional to acceleration)

5 charts or diagrams used for that topic (velocity/time graphs; tape charts)

6 important formulae $\left(\text{acceleration} = \dfrac{\text{change in velocity}}{\text{time}}\right)$.

You will also need practice in *calculations*. Try to answer the questions provided at the end of each topic in this booklet *before* you look at the answers. Practice does make perfect, and if you find you have a real problem with a particular topic or technique, ask your teacher for help.

SOME FINAL HINTS

The tape, and the 4-week revision planner enclosed in this booklet, have already suggested ways to help you in revision and in the exam room itself. Here are a few final hints for the exam.

■ Read the *whole question* carefully before writing. There is plenty of time allowed. Don't rush.
■ In *structured questions* you will be guided about the length of answer by the number of lines on the exam paper, or by an indication of the mark scheme – so if a question carries three marks, you need to make three valid points to score full marks.
■ Show *all your working* in a calculation. Write out any formulae, even if they are given on the exam paper. This will help you to avoid making a wrong substitution.
■ Be careful with *units*. Work = force × distance, but the distance must be in metres if the answer is to be in joules. Similarly energy = power × time but the time must be in seconds.
■ Finally, try to relax. Remember that you have already scored marks in your course assessments. The exam is there to find out what you can do. If you are revising carefully you should do very well indeed.

KEY TOPICS

TOPIC 1
FORCES AND THEIR EFFECTS

T In the tape you were reminded that any **force** can cause an object to change its size or movement, and that all forces are measured in newtons (N). **Weight** is an important force. It is the pull of the Earth, or any planet, on a mass. The Earth pulls each kilogram of mass with a 10 newton force. This force on a kilogram is called the Earth's **gravitational field strength**. It is written $g = 10\,\text{N/kg}$.

So   20 kilograms of mass has a weight of 200 N
and   5 kilograms of mass has a weight of 50 N
            100 grams is 0.1 kg so its weight is just 1 N.

RESULTANT FORCES

Forces are described as **vector** quantities. This means that the effect they have on an object will depend not just on the *size* of the force, but on the *direction* as well. Quantities like volume and temperature do not have any direction, and are called **scalar** quantities.

For example two forces of 3N and 4N can combine to give an overall (**resultant**) force of 7N or 1N depending on how they act (*Fig 1.1(a), (b)*). If they act at an *angle (Fig 1.1 (c))* a **scale drawing** is needed to find the resultant.

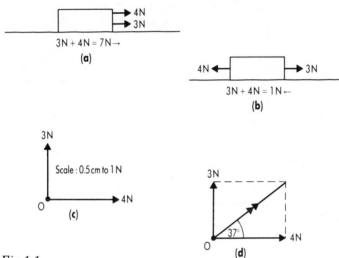

Fig 1.1

Draw a scale diagram showing the forces acting on the object O. State the scale you are using. Complete the rectangle as shown by the dotted lines in *Fig 1.1(d)*. The diagonal is the size of the resultant force, in this case 2.5 cm long, so the force is 5N. It acts at 37° to the horizontal; the diagram gives both the size and direction of the resultant.

MOMENTS OF FORCES

If an object is *pivoted* or *hinged*, forces acting on it can cause a *turning effect*. The turning effect of a force is called the **moment** of the force. The moment depends on both the size of the force and the distance of the force from the pivot. It is measured in newton-metres (N m) or newton-centimetres (N cm) (*Fig 1.2*).

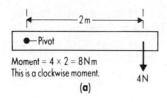

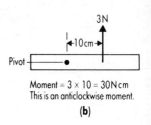

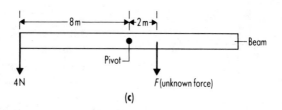

Fig 1.2

BALANCING OF FORCES

For an object to be **balanced** (in equilibrium) the *clockwise moments* must balance the *anticlockwise moments*, otherwise the object would turn in one direction or the other about its pivot. This can be used to solve problems about balance. In *Fig 1.2(c)* the force F needed to keep the beam balanced can be found like this:

anticlockwise moment $= (4 \times 8) = 32 \, \text{Nm}$
clockwise moment $\quad = (F \times 2)$

For balance, clockwise moment = anticlockwise moment
$F \times 2 = 32 \qquad \therefore F = 16 \, \text{N}$

The *weight* of an object can also contribute a turning effect. Weight acts at the **centre of gravity** of an object. This is the same as the geometric centre for a regular solid shape.

PRACTICE QUESTION

Figure 1.3(a) shows a machine used in the construction industry to test samples of dry mortar. The mortar sample is glued between the beam and the fixed platform.

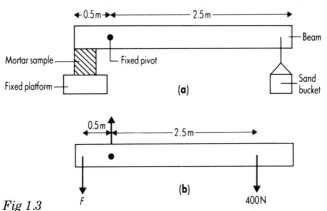

Fig 1.3

a) The pull of the Earth on the sand is 400 N. Use an arrow to mark on the diagram the direction and point of action of this force.
b) Calculate the moment of this force about the fixed pivot.
c) *Figure 1.3(b)* shows the forces acting on the beam. Calculate the size of force *F*. (Ignore the weight of the beam.)   *LEAG (Paper 2)*

Outline Answer

a) The direction is vertically down. The point of action is the centre of gravity of the sand bucket, i.e. its midpoint.
b) Moment = force × distance = 400 × 2.5 = 1000 Nm
c) For balance   clockwise moment = anticlockwise moment.
$$1000 = F \times 0.5$$
$$F = 2000\,\text{N}$$

STUDENT'S ANSWER
with ❝examiner's comments❞

a)

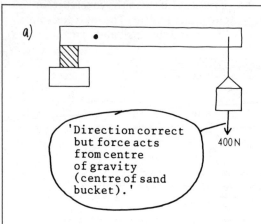

'Direction correct but force acts from centre of gravity (centre of sand bucket).'

400 N

b) $Moment = F \times d = 1000$ ✓

'Unit missing. Could lose a mark here.'

c) $400 \times 2.5 = F \times 0.5$ ✓

$$F = \frac{1000}{0.5} = 500N$$

'Arithmetic error. $1000 \div 0.5 = 2000$.'

TOPIC 2
ENERGY, WORK AND POWER

ENERGY

Energy is a property of an object which enables it to do a job of work. Energy cannot be made or destroyed, but it can *change* from one form to another. This is called **conservation of energy**. The forms of energy are:

chemical

heat (random thermal)

kinetic (movement)

light (electromagnetic wave)

nuclear

sound

electrical

potential (gravitational or strain)

A **machine** is something which can change energy from one form into another. For instance a car changes chemical energy in its fuel into heat and kinetic energy.

POTENTIAL ENERGY

Potential energy is a little harder to understand. It means 'energy waiting to change'. An object lifted above the ground by a pulley and held there has *gravitational* potential energy, which can be changed to *kinetic* energy simply by releasing the string. A bow fitted with an arrow has *strain* potential energy which changes to *kinetic* energy in the arrow.

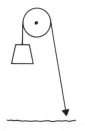

A weight lifted above the ground has gravitational potential energy.

A stretched bow has strain potential energy.

Fig 2.1

Gravitational potential energy is energy which an object has because of its position above the ground. **Strain potential energy** is energy stored in a stretched wire, rubber band etc.

WORK

If something has energy it can do **work**. When work gets done, a *force moves*. The *amount of work* can be calculated from the *size of the force* and the *distance it moves*.

work = force × distance

If the *force* is measured in newtons and the *distance* is measured in metres, then the *unit of work* is joules (J); e.g. if a 4 kg mass is lifted 6 metres above the ground, then work done = (force on 4 kg) × (distance) = 40 N × 6 m = 240 J.

When this work is done the mass has gained potential energy. The energy it now has is equal to the work that was done.

So measuring work is *exactly the same* as measuring an energy change. If the mass fell to the ground, the 240 J of potential energy would change to 240 J of kinetic energy, and, when it hit the ground, to 240 J of heat and sound.

POWER

Power is the rate of energy conversion, or the rate of doing work.

$$\text{power} = \frac{\text{energy change}}{\text{time}} = \frac{\text{work done}}{\text{time}}$$

If the time is measured in seconds, the power is measured in watts (W).

1 watt = 1 joule per second

A powerful motor is therefore one which can do a job quickly, the more powerful it is, the less time the work takes, and the quicker the transfer of energy.

e.g. A motor lifts a 400 N load up a height of 12 m in 1 minute.

The work done = 400 × 12 = 4800 J

The power $\quad = \dfrac{4800}{60} = 80\,\text{W}$

(Note that 1 minute is changed to 60 seconds!)

PRACTICE QUESTION

a) Explain what is meant by the terms *work*, *energy* and *power*, stating the units in which each is measured.

b) Describe in detail an experiment a pupil could do to measure the average power he or she can develop over a period of a few seconds.

c) A crane, whose engines can develop a power of 2 kW is used to raise a 400 kg load from the ground to a platform 12 metres above the ground.
 i) Determine the work done in raising the load on to the platform.
 ii) Determine the minimum time for the crane to raise the load on to the platform.
 iii) Determine the minimum time for the crane to raise a load of 100 kg on to the same platform.

d) State what is meant by *conservation of energy*. Discuss how the idea of energy conservation can be applied to the example of the crane in part (**c**).

NISEC (Paper 3)

Outline Answer

a) Work is done when a force moves through a distance. Measured in joules.
 Energy is the ability to do work. Measured in joules.
 Power is the rate of doing work, or the rate of energy transfer. Measured in watts.

b) A typical method would be to do 'step-ups' on a low gym bench over a timed period. The pupil needs to measure his or her weight using for example bathroom scales calibrated in newtons or to convert their mass in kilograms using $g = 10\,\text{N/kg}$. The height of the bench should be measured with a metre rule graduated in centimetres and millimetres. The height must be converted to metres e.g. $35\,\text{cm} = 0.35\,\text{m}$. Finally, step-ups are done over a timed period of, say, 10 seconds. The number of steps must be counted.

$$\text{Then power} = \frac{\text{weight} \times \text{bench height} \times \text{number of steps}}{\text{time in seconds}}$$

c)   *i*) Work done = force × distance = $4000 \times 12 = 48\,000\,\text{J}$

    ii) $\text{Power} = \dfrac{\text{work}}{\text{time}}$

      $\text{Time} = \dfrac{\text{work}}{\text{power}} = \dfrac{48\,000}{2000} = 24$ seconds

    iii) New time taken $= \dfrac{12\,000}{2000} = 6$ seconds

(Notice in this answer that the mass in kg is converted to weight in N, and the power in kW is converted to watts.)

d)   Conservation of energy means that energy cannot be made or destroyed, only changed from one form to another. If the crane in part (**c**) had a diesel engine, energy would exist at the start as chemical energy in its fuel. This is converted to heat and kinetic energy when the motor runs. The mass is moved upwards, so the mass also obtains kinetic energy and as it rises, potential energy. All the energy forms originally came from the chemical energy in the fuel.

STUDENT'S ANSWER
with 6 examiner's comments 9

'If using letters like this you should explain what they mean.'

'A common error, confusing a fuel with energy forms.'

a) Work = F × d ✓ newtons
Energy is like Coal or oil joules
Power = work ÷ time watts

b) Well he or she could run up some stairs and measure the time.

'No real detail here about how to obtain the measurements, or what, apart from the time, is required to find the power.'

'Good, converted to newtons.'

c) i) 4000 × 12 = 48 000 J ✓

ii) 2 = 48 000 / Time

'Forgot to change kW to watts.'

∴ Time = 48 000 / 2 = 24 000 seconds

'Method correct so some marks gained.'

iii) Work = 1000 × 12 = 12000 W
Time = 12000 / 2 = 6000 seconds

'Unit should be J.'

'Same mistake so no loss of marks this time.'

d) Conservation means energy is always there and cannot be lost. ✓
The fuel in the crane turns to energy in the mass. ✓

'Should be the energy in the fuel.'

'Not enough detail about the sequence of energy changes, though what is said is correct, more or less.'

TOPIC 3
LINEAR MOTION

T From the tape, you should have a clear idea of the meaning of the terms velocity and acceleration. In this section we shall look at how to calculate their values from graphs and data.

VELOCITY

$$\text{velocity} = \frac{\text{distance travelled}}{\text{time}} \quad \text{measured in m/s.}$$

If the distance travelled in each second of a journey remains the same, then the **velocity** is steady, and is called *constant velocity* (*Fig 3.1(a)*).

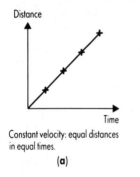

Constant velocity: equal distances in equal times.

(a)

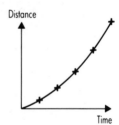

Acceleration: the distances travelled in equal times get larger and larger.

(b)

Fig 3.1

ACCELERATION

If the velocity increases all the time, then an object is **accelerating** and will cover greater and greater distances in each succeeding second (*Fig 3.1(b)*).

$$\text{acceleration} = \frac{\text{change in velocity}}{\text{time}} \quad \text{measured in m/s}^2$$

So if a car changes velocity from 20 m/s to 40 m/s in 5 seconds its acceleration is $\dfrac{(40-20)}{5} = 4\,\text{m/s}^2$. Such calculations are often made from *graphical data*, as shown in *Fig 3.2*.

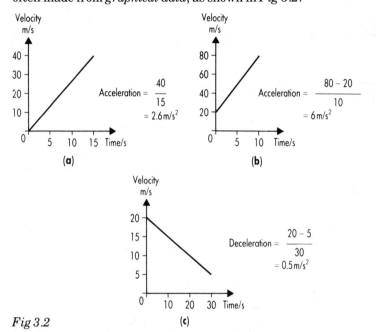

Fig 3.2

Using some algebra in the definition of velocity gives an *equation useful for calculating velocity or acceleration*. If a vehicle has a starting velocity u, a final velocity after a time t of v, and its acceleration is a, then

$$a = \frac{v - u}{t} \quad \text{and} \quad v = u + at.$$

DISTANCE TRAVELLED

Graphs of velocity and time also enable the *distance travelled* by an object to be calculated; the distance is the area under the graph (*Fig 3.3*).

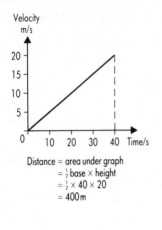

Distance = area under graph
= ½ base × height
= ½ × 40 × 20
= 400 m

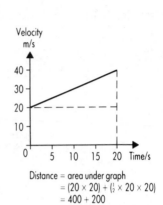

Distance = area under graph
= (20 × 20) + (½ × 20 × 20)
= 400 + 200
= 600 m

Fig 3.3

Again, if some algebra is applied to a similar 'area under the graph' problem, we obtain a general *equation for calculating distance travelled.*

$s = ut + \frac{1}{2}at^2$ where s = distance.

For an object starting from rest this simplifies to

$s = \frac{1}{2}at^2$

FORCE AND ACCELERATION

Acceleration is only possible if a resultant force acts on an object. The greater the force, the greater the acceleration. However the *mass* to be accelerated has an effect, and a greater force is needed to accelerate a large mass to the same value as a small mass. Thus

force = mass × acceleration
or $F = ma$

When no force is acting, as in space or on a laboratory frictionless air track, there is no acceleration and an object moves with constant velocity.

Similarly if the forces acting are all balanced, there is no acceleration since again there is no resultant force. This happens to parachutists when their weight acting towards the Earth is balanced by the upward air friction force on the parachute.

PRACTICE QUESTION

A cycle track is 500 metres long. A cyclist completes 10 laps (that is rides completely round the track 10 times).
a)   How many kilometres has the cyclist travelled?
b)   On average it took the cyclist 50 seconds to complete one lap.
   i)   What was the average speed of the cyclist?
   ii)   How long in minutes and seconds did it take the cyclist to complete the 10 laps?
c)   Near the end of the run the cyclist put on a spurt. During this spurt it took the cyclist 2 seconds to increase speed from 8 m/s to 12 m/s. What was the cyclist's acceleration during this spurt?

SEG (Paper 2)

Outline Answer

a)   Total distance in metres = $10 \times 500 = 5000$ m
   1 km = 1000 m   So distance is 5 km.

b)   *i*)   Average speed = $\dfrac{\text{distance}}{\text{time}} = \dfrac{500}{50} = 10$ m/s

   ii)   Total distance = 5000 m
      At 10 m/s this will take 5000/10 seconds = 500 s

      Time is $\dfrac{500}{60} = 8\frac{1}{3}$ minutes = 8 minutes 20 seconds

c)   Acceleration = $\dfrac{\text{velocity change}}{\text{time}} = \dfrac{(12-8)}{2} = 2$ m/s^2

STUDENT'S ANSWER
with ❝examiner's comments❞

a) Distance = 10 × 500 = 5000 (km)

'UNITS! The value should be in metres.'

b) i) Speed = $\frac{500}{50}$ = 10 m/s ✓

'The candidate did not read the whole question. It's the time for 10 laps that is asked for.'

ii) Distance = 500m

'Correct method applied, which will gain marks despite the wrong answer.'

∴ Time = $\frac{500}{10}$ = 5 seconds ✗

c) a = $\frac{v-u}{t}$ = $\frac{12-8}{2}$

= 2 m/s² ✓

TOPIC 4
WAVE MOTION

PROPERTIES OF WAVES

T ▶ You should be sure of the meanings of the terms *amplitude*, *wavelength* and *frequency* as applied to a wave, and be aware of the *wave equation*.

velocity = frequency × wavelength
$$v = f \times \lambda$$

where velocity is in m/s, frequency is in Hz, wavelength is in m.

Figure 4.1 should help you to remember some important points.

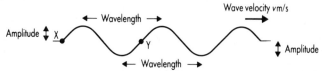

XY represents one complete cycle of the wave.
Frequency, in hertz, is the number of cycles per second.

Fig 4.1

Sound, which is a longitudinal wave, is usually examined using a microphone attached to an oscilloscope, so that the pattern shown on the screen relates to the pressure changes in the wave. A *loud* sound is shown to have a *large amplitude* and a *high-pitched* sound is one with a *large frequency*. Different musical instruments, playing the same note, sound different because they produce different wave forms. This is described as different 'quality' of notes.

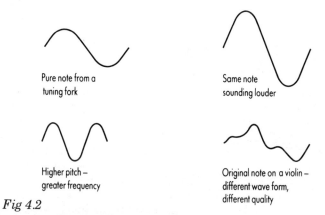

Pure note from a
tuning fork

Same note
sounding louder

Higher pitch –
greater frequency

Original note on a violin –
different wave form,
different quality

Fig 4.2

REFLECTION AND REFRACTION

All waves can be *reflected*. In the case of sound the reflection is an **echo**, and this can be used to measure the speed of sound, or in echo-sounding to find, for example, the depth of the sea-bed.

Both sound and light *change velocity* when they travel from one material to another, and water waves change velocity when the depth of the water changes. This velocity change can also give a change of direction if the wave approaches the new material at an angle. This *direction change* is called **refraction**.

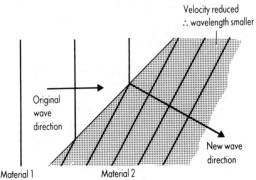

Fig 4.3

INTERFERENCE AND DIFFRACTION

The two most important wave properties are **interference** and **diffraction**. They are important because they are unique to waves, and can be used to prove whether an energy transfer takes place by wave motion or not.

When waves *overlap* they combine to give either an increased (*constructive interference*) or decreased (*destructive interference*) amplitude. If the two waves had originally the *same* amplitude, frequency and wavelength this can result in a double amplitude wave, *or* in *cancellation*. This is shown in *Fig 4.4* (opposite).

When waves pass through a gap in a barrier they spread out beyond the edges of the barrier. This is called *diffraction* (as shown in *Fig 4.5*, opposite). The smaller the gap the greater the amount of diffraction; the amount of diffraction increases as the wavelength of the wave increases.

Constructive interference: waves in phase combine to give an increased amplitude.

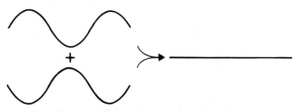

Destructive interference: every point on one wave is cancelled by a point in the other, giving no wave motion.

Fig 4.4

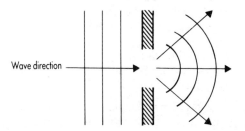

Wave direction

Fig 4.5

ELECTROMAGNETIC WAVES

The group of waves, which includes visible light, is called the **electromagnetic spectrum**. Waves of this type can be classified according to their wavelength. The shortest wavelengths are called gamma (γ) waves, then come X rays, ultra violet, visible light, infra red and radio waves. They all travel *at the same speed* of 3×10^8 m/s and unlike all other waves they do *not* need a material to travel through – they can travel in a vacuum. They are all *transverse* waves and consist of oscillating electric and magnetic fields.

PRACTICE QUESTION

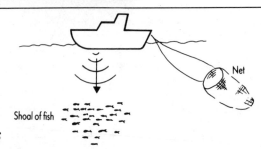

Fig 4.6

Figure 4.6 shows a fishing vessel using a sonar system to detect a shoal of fish.

A short pulse of sound waves is emitted vertically downwards from the ship. These waves have a frequency of 500 Hz and wavelength 3 m in water, and the echo from the shoal of fish is detected 0.1 s later.

i) Calculate the velocity of the sound wave in water.
ii) At what depth should the nets be trawled? Show clearly how you obtain your answer.
iii) In practice the duration of the reflected pulse is greater than that of the emitted pulse. Suggest one reason why this is so.

The diagram below shows the main regions of the electromagnetic spectrum (not drawn to scale).

Radio waves	Micro waves	A	Visible	Ultra violet	B	Gamma rays

iv) What type of radiation exists in regions A and B?
v) What portion of the spectrum is used to transmit messages to astronauts in a space station orbiting the earth?
vi) Why is it not possible to use sound waves to transmit messages to astronauts in a space station?

NISEC (Paper 2)

Outline Answer

i) Velocity = frequency × wavelength = $500 \times 3 = 1500$ m/s
ii) Waves take 0.1 seconds to travel to the shoal and back.
   Distance to shoal and back = $1500 \times 0.1 = 150$ m
   Distance to shoal from boat = $150 \div 2 = 75$ m
   Trawl net at 75 m depth.
iii) The pulse will reflect off several 'layers' of fish in the shoal, so some parts will travel further than others, resulting in a longer duration of the reflected pulse.
iv) A is infra red, B is X rays.
v) Radio waves.
vi) Sound cannot travel in space (a vacuum); it must be transmitted through a material.

STUDENT'S ANSWER
with 6 examiner's comments 9

i) $v = f\lambda = 500 \times 3 = 1500$ m/s ✓

ii) Distance = Velocity × Time
   $= 1500 \times 0.1$
   $= 150$ m ✓

'Correct so far. But this is the distance to the shoal and back!'

iii) The reflected pulse is slower <u>because it has travelled through the water.</u>

'Makes no difference. The speed in water is constant at 1500 m/s. Possibly the candidate did not understand the word 'duration' meaning 'length of time'.'

iv) A = Infra red ✓
   B = Ultra violet ✗

v) Radio ✓

vi) Sound waves are longitudinal, radio waves are transverse. ✗

'The statement is true but it is not the reason why sound cannot be used.'

TOPIC 5
DIRECT CURRENT

Remember the definitions you heard on the tape:
- **current** is a flow of charge, measured in amps
- **1 amp** = 1 coulomb of charge per second
- **voltage** is the measurement of the energy of each charge
- **1 volt** = 1 joule of energy per coulomb
- **power** is the rate of energy transfer, measured in watts
- **1 watt** = 1 joule of energy per second

$$\text{power} = \text{current} \times \text{voltage}$$
$$P = I \times V$$

POWER AND ENERGY

Many electrical devices have the *power rating* marked on them, so if you know what the *supply voltage* is you can calculate the *current*. E.g. in a laboratory with a 12 V power supply, a 36 W bulb will take a current $I = P/V = 36/12 = 3$ A.

This is especially important in household appliances which operate from the 240 V mains. A three-pin mains plug has a fuse in the live side and it is vital for safety that the fuse has the correct value. Fuses supplied are rated at 3 A, 5 A and 13 A.

Use the equation to find the normal working current for an appliance and choose the next highest fuse value.

A 2 kW electric fire would have a current of 2000/240 = 8.3 A. Use a 13 A fuse.
A 400 W stereo system has a current of 400/240 = 1.6 A. Use a 3 A fuse.

The power of an appliance also dictates the *energy* you are consuming since energy = power × time. The Electricity Board has to be paid for this energy and they calculate the cost in '**units**'. 1 unit is used when a 1 kW appliance is run for 1 hour. So to count the cost you multiply the power in kilowatts by the time in hours. This gives the number of units, and each unit costs about 5p.

ELECTRICAL MEASUREMENTS

Most electrical measurements involve connecting an *ammeter* and a *voltmeter* in a circuit. Ammeters go in *series*, and voltmeters in *parallel* across the component you want to know about (*Fig 5.1*).

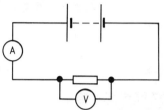

Fig 5.1

In the circuit of *Fig 5.1*, you can obviously find the power dissipated in the resistor since $P = IV$. If the voltage is varied in steps, and a graph drawn of the way the current changes with voltage, it is a straight line (*Fig 5.2(a)*). This means that **voltage is proportional to current**, or $V \propto I$. So doubling the voltage doubles the current. This can be put in equation form as $V = IR$ where R is the **resistance**, which in this case is constant. Resistances are not always constant. A light bulb gets hotter as the current in it rises and its resistance rises as well (*Fig 5.2(b)*).

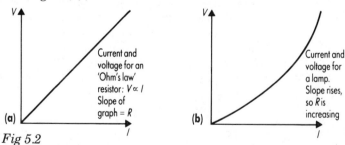

(a) Current and voltage for an 'Ohm's law' resistor: $V \propto I$. Slope of graph = R

(b) Current and voltage for a lamp. Slope rises, so R is increasing

Fig 5.2

Resistance is measured in ohms (Ω); if the resistance of a wire is 1 Ω, this means that 1 volt would be needed *across* the wire to drive 1 amp through it.

If several resistors are linked in *series* the net effect is found by *adding* their values, e.g. 100 Ω and 60 Ω give the same effect as a single resistor of 160 Ω.

However in *parallel* they behave differently, giving a new lower value. If resistors are in parallel, and the net effect is the same as a single value R, then

$$\frac{1}{R} = \frac{1}{R_1} + \frac{1}{R_2}$$

Suppose $R_1 = R_2 = 10\,\Omega$ and they are in parallel; then

$$\frac{1}{R} = \frac{1}{10} + \frac{1}{10} = \frac{2}{10} \qquad R = 5\,\Omega$$

The *combination* behaves like a *single* $5\,\Omega$ resistor.

PRACTICE QUESTION

a) In *Fig 5.3* join together the components so that the lamp may be switched on or off by either switch.

b) A certain lamp is rated 12 V 36 W.
    i) Calculate the current taken by this lamp when connected to a 12 V battery.
    ii) Calculate the resistance of the lamp under normal working conditions.

c) A light-emitting diode (LED) is connected in series with a 5 V battery as shown in *Fig 5.4*.
    i) What is the purpose of the 180 Ω resistor?
    ii) A voltmeter connected across the 180 Ω reads 3.6 volts. Calculate the current in this circuit.
    iii) Why is the reading on the voltmeter less than 5 V? What happens to the remaining 1.4 V?

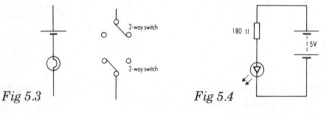

Fig 5.3

Fig 5.4

LEAG (Paper 2)

Outline Answer

Fig 5.5

a) See *Fig 5.5*.

b) i) Power = current × voltage

Current = $\dfrac{\text{power}}{\text{voltage}} = \dfrac{36}{12} = 3\,\text{A}$

 ii) Resistance = $\dfrac{\text{voltage}}{\text{current}} = \dfrac{12}{3} = 4\,\Omega$

c) i) A light-emitting diode is a semi conductor device. As it gets hotter its resistance drops so it conducts more current, gets even hotter and so on. The $180\,\Omega$ resistor is there to limit the current and protect the LED.

 ii) $I = V/R = 3.6/180 = 0.02\,\text{A}$ or $20\,\text{mA}$

 iii) Voltage readings are about energy changes. Some energy is also converted in the LED, 1.4 joules per coulomb.

STUDENT'S ANSWER
with 6examiner's comments 9

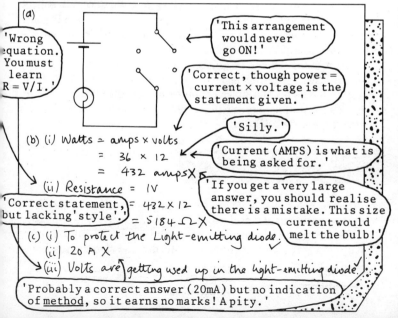

(a)

'This arrangement would never go ON!'

'Wrong equation. You must learn R = V/I.'

'Correct, though power = current × voltage is the statement given.'

(b) (i) Watts = amps × volts
= 36 × 12
= 432 amps✗

'Silly.'

'Current (AMPS) is what is being asked for.'

(ii) Resistance = 1V
= 432 × 12
= 5184 Ω✗

'Correct statement, but lacking 'style'.'

'If you get a very large answer, you should realise there is a mistake. This size current would melt the bulb!'

(c) (i) To protect the Light-emitting diode.
(ii) 20 A ✗
(iii) Volts are getting used up in the light-emitting diode ✓

'Probably a correct answer (20mA) but no indication of <u>method</u>, so it earns no marks! A pity.'

TOPIC 6
KINETIC THEORY AND HEAT ENERGY

Kinetic theory uses a simplified model of an atom to explain some of the differences in behaviour of solids, liquids and gases.

NATURE AND EFFECT OF PARTICLES

Solids have strong forces of attraction and repulsion between particles, giving them *rigidity*, and making them hard to compress. **Liquids** have forces which are a little weaker between particles, enabling a liquid to *flow*. **Gases** have forces which are negligible between particles, since the particles are so far apart.

In all these states, particles are *moving*, though in a solid the movement is restricted to vibration about fixed points. The *movement of particles in a gas* can explain diffusion, Brownian motion, and the pressure and volume changes of a gas as its temperature is varied.

Temperature can be related to the average kinetic energy of particles. It is different from **heat**, which is an energy form and depends on the mass of material present. Thermometers are calibrated by taking two fixed points, *ice point* (0°C) and *steam point* (100°C).

SPECIFIC HEAT CAPACITY AND LATENT HEAT

When a *solid* is heated its temperature rises as its particles gain kinetic energy and vibrate more strongly. The temperature rise produced depends on the solid's **specific heat capacity**. This is the amount of energy needed to raise the temperature of 1 kg by 1°C.

$$\text{heat energy} = \text{mass} \times \frac{\text{specific heat}}{\text{capacity}} \times \frac{\text{temperature}}{\text{rise}}$$

As the solid gets hotter there comes a point when the energy provided is used to *break* the bonds between the particles and the solid *melts*. At the melting point there is *no* change of temperature. The same applies when a liquid boils, the energy provided is used to break the bonds holding the liquid together and releases the particles into the gas state. The energy supplied to change the state of matter *without* raising its temperature is called the **latent heat**.

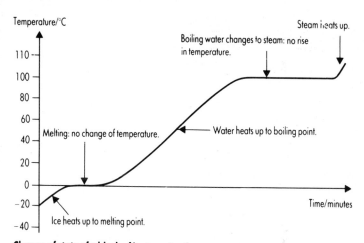

Change of state of a block of ice to water then steam

Fig 6.1

PRESSURE, VOLUME AND TEMPERATURE

When a *gas* is heated, both its pressure and volume may change. Experiments are therefore usually designed to change *one* variable at a time. If the gas is heated in a closed container, the volume is fixed and only the *pressure* changes. If the gas is heated in a cylinder with a freely moving piston, the pressure is fixed and only the *volume* changes. The pattern of change is the *same* in each case (*Fig 6.2*) and the graphs can be extended to $-273°C$ (**absolute zero**) at which the particles are at rest, and exert no pressure.

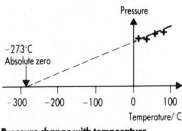 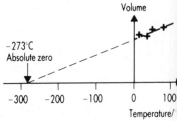

Pressure change with temperature
(volume kept constant)

Volume change with temperature
(pressure kept constant)

Fig 6.2

The pressure and volume relationships as temperature rises can be summarised as

$$\frac{P_1}{P_2} = \frac{T_1}{T_2} \quad \text{and} \quad \frac{V_1}{V_2} = \frac{T_1}{T_2} \ (T \text{ is in kelvins.})$$

$-273°C$ is called 0 kelvin so $0°C$ is $273\,K$ and $100°C$ is $373\,K$.

TRANSFER OF HEAT ENERGY

Heat energy can be *transferred* in one of these ways:
- **conduction** mainly in metallic solids; energy is transferred by vibrating particles
- **convection** in liquids and gases, caused by density changes in the warm material
- **radiation** electromagnetic waves which can travel through space, emitted from hot objects.

PRACTICE QUESTION

a) What is meant by the statement that the specific heat capacity of water is $4200\,J/kg°C$?
b) *i*) A 50 W heater is totally immersed in water which is contained in an aluminium pot. The heater is switched on and the initial and final

temperature of the water noted over a period of
time. From the following, determine the specific
heat capacity of the water, showing clearly how
you obtain your answer.
Mass of water = 2.5 kg
Initial temperature of water = 20°C
Final temperature of water = 28°C
Time for which the heater was operating = 30
minutes

ii) Suggest two reasons why the value for the
specific heat capacity calculated above differs
from the true value given in **a**). (Assume that all
readings have been taken accurately and that
the heater was tested to give 50 W precisely.)

NISEC (Paper 3)

Outline Answer

a) The statement means that 4200 J of heat energy are
needed to raise the temperature of 1 kg of water by 1°C.

b) i) Energy provided = power × time = 50 × 30 × 60
= 90 000 J

$$\text{Energy} = \text{mass} \times \frac{\text{specific heat}}{\text{capacity}} \times \frac{\text{temperature}}{\text{rise}}$$

$$\text{Specific heat capacity} = \frac{\text{energy}}{\text{mass} \times \text{temperature rise}}$$

$$\text{Specific heat capacity} = \frac{90000}{2.5 \times (28 - 20)}$$

$$= \frac{90000}{2.5 \times 8} = 4500 \, \text{J/kg}°\text{C}$$

ii) Two possible reasons are:
- some of the energy provided goes to heat the
aluminium pot rather than the water. This is not
accounted for in the calculation.
- over this long time, heat is also lost to the atmosphere from both the water and the pot.

STUDENT'S ANSWER

with ❝examiner's comments❞

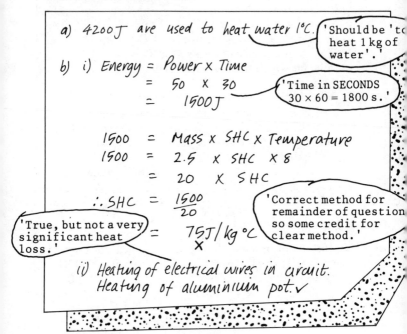

a) 4200J are used to heat water 1°C.   'Should be 'to heat 1 kg of water'.'

b) i) Energy = Power × Time
         = 50 × 30
         = 1500 J   'Time in SECONDS 30 × 60 = 1800 s.'

   1500 = Mass × SHC × Temperature
   1500 = 2.5 × SHC × 8
        = 20 × SHC

   ∴ SHC = 1500/20
           = 75 J/kg °C ✗   'Correct method for remainder of question so some credit for clear method.'

   'True, but not a very significant heat loss.'

   ii) Heating of electrical wires in circuit.
       Heating of aluminium pot. ✓

TOPIC 7
ELECTROMAGNETISM AND A.C.

MAGNETIC FIELDS

T When an electric current flows in a wire, a **magnetic field** is produced. The field *strength* depends on the size of current and the number of turns of wire, its *direction* depends on the current direction. You should be familiar with the *field shapes* shown in *Fig 7.1*.

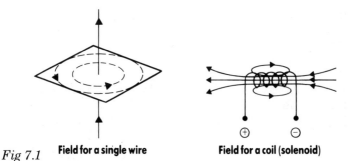

Fig 7.1   **Field for a single wire**   **Field for a coil (solenoid)**

If the wire or coil carrying the current is in a magnetic field region, there is a *force* on the wire which can cause movement. The greatest force occurs when the current and field are at 90° to each other. The force itself is at 90° to both field and current (Fleming's left hand rule, *Fig 7.2*).

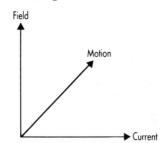

Fig 7.2

A *motor* uses this principle, and continuous rotation is possible using a split ring commutator which reverses the current every 180° turn. *Moving coil ammeters* also depend on this idea since the force is proportional to the current in the coil.

GENERATING ELECTRICAL ENERGY

The motor situation is an energy conversion from electrical to kinetic. **Generating electricity** uses the *reverse* idea. A wire *moved* in a magnetic field has an e.m.f. induced in it, and a current can flow; alternatively, a *stationary* wire has an e.m.f.

induced in it by a changing field. A **dynamo** acts as a motor in reverse, giving a changing current as the coil rotates. The voltage induced in the coil, and therefore the current flow, depends on the connection between the coil and the external circuit. A **slip ring commutator** gives a voltage varying in size and direction (*Fig 7.3(a)*); a **split ring commutator** gives variation in size but in *one direction only* (*Fig 7.3(b)*).

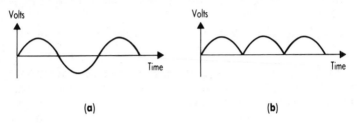

(a)   **(b)**

Fig 7.3

The **size** of the induced voltage depends on the *number of turns* of wire in the dynamo coil, the *strength* of the magnets or electromagnets, and the *speed* with which the wire cuts through the magnetic field. Doubling the speed of a dynamo will change the frequency of the output voltage and also make it larger.

TRANSFORMERS AND THE NATIONAL GRID

Transformers use changing magnetic fields to 'step up' or 'step down' voltages. The two coils are called *primary* and *secondary*. An alternating voltage applied to the primary coil causes an alternating voltage in the secondary, but the *size* of the secondary voltage depends on the *ratio* of the number of primary turns to secondary turns. The rule is

$$\frac{V_{primary}}{V_{secondary}} = \frac{N_{primary}}{N_{secondary}}$$

where V = voltage and N = number of turns.

If there are *more* secondary turns than primary turns the voltage is *stepped up* (increased). However energy must be conserved, so the secondary current would be less than the primary, and always

primary power = secondary power
$$I_\mathrm{p}V_\mathrm{p} = I_\mathrm{s}V_\mathrm{s}$$

In practice transformers are not 100% efficient and there will be some energy losses.

The **National Grid** system uses transformers to transmit electrical energy over large distances. Transmission is at high voltage and low current to reduce energy loss by heating of the transmission wires. The voltage is stepped down to 240 V before being supplied for use in the home. Obviously transmission is a.c. since a transformer depends for its action on a changing magnetic field.

PRACTICE QUESTION

a)   A coil of wire is connected to a battery and a switch as shown in *Fig 7.4*.

Fig 7.4

   i)   Draw on the diagram the shape of the magnetic field in and surrounding the coil when the switch is closed. Clearly mark the current direction and the field direction.

   ii)   How would this arrangement have to be changed to form an electromagnet?

   iii)   Name one practical device which uses an electromagnet.

b)   Two metal rods are placed inside a coil as shown in *Fig 7.5*.

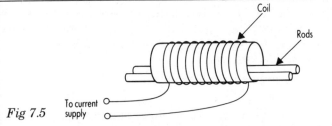

Fig 7.5

To current supply

When direct current flows in the coil the rods move apart, but when the current is switched off they return to their original positions.

i) Why do the rods move apart?
ii) From what metal could the rods have been made? Explain your choice.
iii) If alternating current (a.c.) from a mains transformer was used, instead of direct current (d.c.), what effect (if any) would this have on the rods? Explain your answer.

c) *Figure 7.6* shows a heavy copper rod, freely suspended on thin base copper wires between the poles of a magnet. The ends of the suspension wires are connected to the input of an oscilloscope which is suitably adjusted with its time base on.

i) Explain why a voltage is induced across the rod when it is swinging between the poles of the magnet.

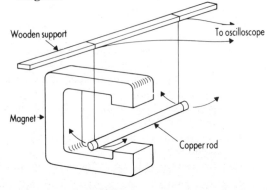

Fig 7.6

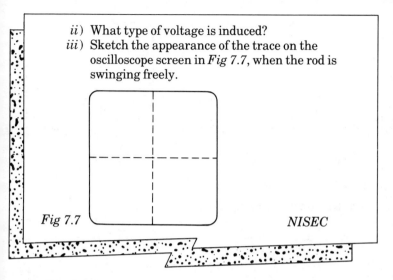

ii) What type of voltage is induced?

iii) Sketch the appearance of the trace on the oscilloscope screen in *Fig 7.7*, when the rod is swinging freely.

Fig 7.7

NISEC

Outline Answer

a) *i*) See *Fig 7.8*.

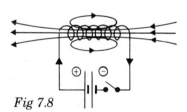

Fig 7.8

ii) A soft iron metal core should be inserted in the coil.

iii) Electric bell, relay, etc.

b) *i*) With d.c. the two rods are magnetised in the same direction so similar poles are together and repel.

ii) Soft iron. Since the rods return to their original position when the current is switched off, a magnetic material which loses its magnetism easily must have been used.

iii) The rods would vibrate, being magnetised in opposite directions 100 times a second, and losing their magnetism when the a.c. passes through zero.

c) *i*) The rod moves in a magnetic field, cutting lines of magnetic flux.

ii) Alternating voltage.
iii) See *Fig 7.9*.

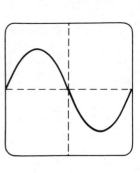

Fig 7.9

STUDENT'S ANSWER
with ❛examiner's comments❜

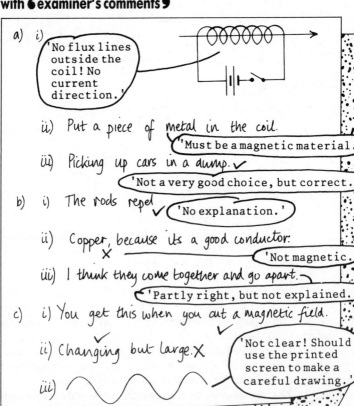

a) i) 'No flux lines outside the coil! No current direction.'

ii) Put a piece of metal in the coil. 'Must be a magnetic material.'

iii) Picking up cars in a dump. ✓ 'Not a very good choice, but correct.'

b) i) The rods repel ✓ 'No explanation.'

ii) Copper, because its a good conductor. ✗ 'Not magnetic.'

iii) I think they come together and go apart. 'Partly right, but not explained.'

c) i) You get this when you cut a magnetic field.

ii) Changing but Large. ✗ 'Not clear! Should use the printed screen to make a careful drawing.'

iii)

T O P I C   8
O P T I C S

Although **light** is an electromagnetic wave, it is convenient to trace its path by drawing guide lines described as *rays*. These show the direction in which the wave travels.

REFLECTION AND REFRACTION

Light, like all waves, can be **reflected**. The rule is 'the angle of incidence is equal to the angle of reflection' and at a mirror surface this results in an *image*. The image appears as far behind the mirror as the object is in front of it. It is a *virtual image* and cannot be put on a screen (*Fig 8.1*).

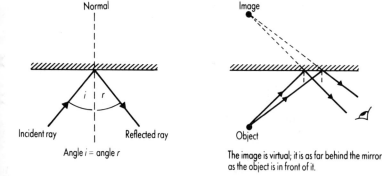

Angle *i* = angle *r*

The image is virtual; it is as far behind the mirror as the object is in front of it.

Fig 8.1

When light travels from the air into a denser transparent material like glass or water, its velocity is reduced and this can cause a change of direction; the effect is called **refraction**. It is refraction which causes objects below a water surface to appear closer to the surface than they really are (*Fig 8.2*).

Light leaving a dense material and entering the air refracts *away* from the normal. As the incident angle increases, **total**

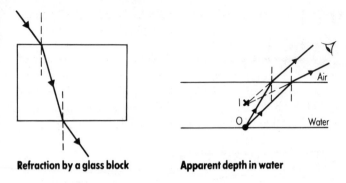

Refraction by a glass block   **Apparent depth in water**

Fig 8.2

internal reflection can occur, and the ray no longer leaves
the material (*Fig 8.3*). For glass this occurs for angles greater
than 42° (the *critical* angle). Total internal reflection is used
in prism periscopes, and in optical fibres to conduct light down
a fibre in some surgical operations.

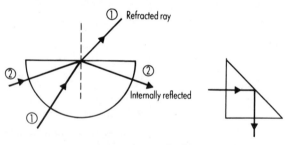

Fig 8.3   **Total internal reflection**

Refraction also occurs at a lens surface, but because of the
curvature of the lens this can lead to focussing. A convex lens
converges light and a concave lens diverges it.

REAL AND VIRTUAL IMAGES

A parallel beam of light is focussed at a point called the
principal focus of a convex lens, F. A ray of light passes

through the centre of a lens without a change of direction. These 'special' rays are used in lens diagrams to predict the position and size of an image.

For a convex lens, a *real image* is formed if the distance of the object from the lens is just greater than its focal length. Real images are inverted, and may be enlarged or diminished depending on the position of the object.

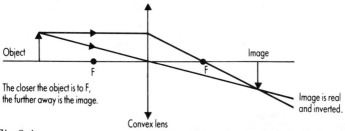

Fig 8.4

An object placed closer to a convex lens than the focal length gives an *enlarged virtual image*. This is the situation when a convex lens is used as a magnifying glass (*Fig 8.5*).

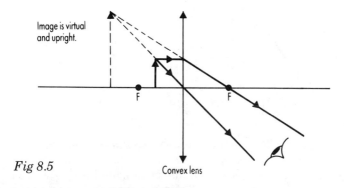

Fig 8.5

DISPERSION

White light consists of a mixture of wavelengths, which give the sensation of white when they fall on the eye. Each wavelength corresponds to a different colour, and white light can be separated into its separate colours with a prism (*Fig 8.6*). This is known as **dispersion**. Apart from the visible wavelengths, invisible infra red and ultra violet can also be detected at the two extreme ends of the spectrum. Infra red is detected with a heat sensitive detector, and ultra violet by fluorescent paper.

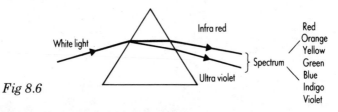

Fig 8.6

PRACTICE QUESTION

i) Complete *Fig 8.7* by drawing two suitable rays to show clearly how the convex lens forms an image of the object. Clearly mark the position of the image (F is the principal focus).

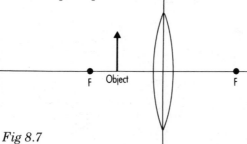

Fig 8.7

ii) Describe the image by underlining the appropriate words.
The image formed is (real/virtual), (upright/inverted) and (magnified/diminished).

iii) Name the optical device which uses a single converging lens to produce an image of this description.

NISEC (Paper 2)

Outline Answer

i) See *Fig. 8.8.*

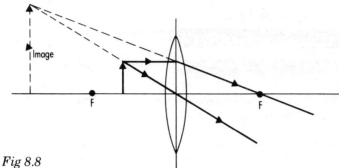

Fig 8.8

ii) The image is virtual, upright and magnified.
iii) A magnifying glass.

STUDENT'S ANSWER

with 6 examiner's comments 9

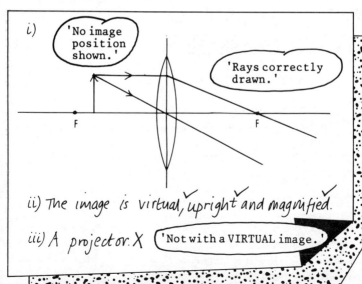

TOPIC 9
DENSITY, PRESSURE AND HYDRAULICS

DENSITY

T ▶ **Density** is defined as mass per unit volume, so it is calculated from the formula

$$d = \frac{m}{v}$$

The units are kg/m^3 or g/cm^3. The density of *water* is 1000 kg/m^3 or 1 g/cm^3.

Measurement of density requires careful volume measurement. The volume of a *regular* solid is easy to calculate, but *irregular* shapes need a water displacement method, using a displacement can and a measuring cylinder.

PRESSURE

Pressure is the effect of a force acting on an area, calculated as

$P = F/A$.

The units are N/m^2 or pascals (Pa). For example,

1000 N of force acting on an area of 0.5 m^2 gives a pressure of 1000/0.5 = 2000 Pa.

1000 N acting on an area of 0.1 m^2 gives a pressure of 1000/0.1 = 10000 Pa.

The larger the area, the smaller the pressure.

In *liquids* pressure increases with depth, and is greater in liquids of high density.

pressure = depth × density × g
where g is gravitational field strength.

So at 100 m depth in water

pressure $= 100 \times 1000 \times 10$
$\qquad = 1\,000\,000\,\text{Pa}$

At a given depth in a liquid the pressure is the *same* in all directions.

Gas pressure is often measured using a *manometer (Fig 9.1)*. The pressure can be expressed in terms of liquid height or in pascals.

The atmosphere exerts a large pressure, equivalent to the pressure below 76 cm depth of mercury. This pressure varies from day to day and can be measured with a *mercury barometer (Fig 9.2)*.

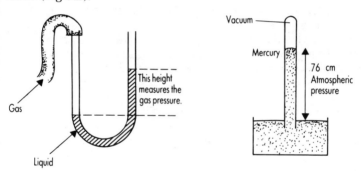

Fig 9.1   *Fig 9.2*

HYDRAULICS

A liquid is not very compressible and can therefore be used to transmit pressure efficiently in hydraulic presses or lifts and in a motor car braking system (*Fig 9.3*).

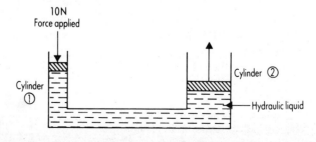

Fig 9.3

A small force applied to cylinder 1 causes a pressure on the liquid. If the area of cylinder 1 is $5\,cm^2$ then a $10\,N$ force will exert a pressure of $10/5 = 2\,N/cm^2$. This transmits to cylinder 2. If its area is $20\,cm^2$ the force exerted will be $2 \times 20 = 40\,N$. So a small applied force results in a larger force at the second cylinder.

Gases are easily compressed. As the pressure increases the volume is reduced, but at a *fixed temperature*, pressure × volume is constant (**Boyle's law**).

PRACTICE QUESTION

Figure 9.4 shows a plastic container for liquid fertiliser as used by gardeners. The container has a built in measure so that the liquid can easily be used in the correct amount. (Throughout the question you are to assume that the density of the liquid is the same as that of water.)

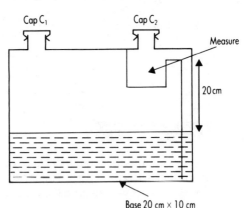

Fig 9.4

Base 20 cm × 10 cm

In order to fill the measure, the sides of the container are squeezed.
  i) State which of C_1 and C_2 should be tightly closed at this stage.
  ii) Explain why.

iii) Calculate how much extra pressure, measured in pascals, (over and above atmospheric) will be needed in the container in order to fill the measure with liquid. (Use $g = 10\,\text{m/s}^2$ and density of water = $1000\,\text{kg/m}^3$.)

iv) Name the type of energy which the liquid would gain by being pushed into the container.

v) In fact the person squeezing the container in order to fill the measure probably supplies more energy than would be accounted for by the energy mentioned in *(iv)*. Give a reason for this.

vi) Suppose the container has a negligible weight and contains 2 litres of liquid. Given the dimensions of the container as shown in *Fig 9.4*, calculate the pressure which it exerts on the ground.
(Use $g = 10\,\text{m/s}^2$ and density of water = $1000\,\text{kg/m}^3$ or $1\,\text{kg/litre}$.)   *LEAG (Paper 2)*

Outline Answer

i) Cap C_1.

ii) When the container is squeezed the pressure of the air above the liquid increases, forcing liquid up into the measure. If C_1 was open, air would simply escape through C_1, with no pressure change.

iii) Pressure = depth × density × g
$$= 0.20 \times 1000 \times 10 = 2000\,\text{Pa}$$

iv) Potential energy.

v) Some energy is required to deform the container.

vi) Pressure = $\dfrac{\text{force}}{\text{area}}$

Mass of liquid = volume × density = $20 \times 1 = 20\,\text{kg}$
Weight of liquid = $200\,\text{N}$
Area of base = $(0.2 \times 0.1)\,\text{m}^2 = 0.02\,\text{m}^2$

Pressure = $\dfrac{200}{0.02} = 10\,000\,\text{Pa}$

STUDENT'S ANSWER
with 6examiner's comments9

i) Cap C_1 ✓

'This doesn't explain why C_1 is closed.'

ii) Otherwise the liquid will not get into the measure.

iii) Pressure = 20 × 1000 × 10

= 200 000 Pa ✗

'Forgot to convert 20 cm into metres.'

iv) Potential energy. ✓

v) Some energy goes into making the person's muscles move. ✓ 'Yes. This does account for it.'

vi) Pressure = force ÷ area

= 10 000 Pa ✓

'Lucky to get the right answer. Wiser to show the steps in a calculation.'

TOPIC 10
ATOMIC STRUCTURE AND RADIOACTIVITY

IONS, PROTONS AND NEUTRONS

An **atom** has a positively charged, very small nucleus, surrounded by negatively charged *electrons*. The total positive charge on the nucleus is balanced by the negative charge, so that usually an atom is electrically neutral. An atom which gains or loses electrons is called an **ion**.

The nucleus itself is made up of two types of particle, **protons** and **neutrons**. They have *equal mass*, but protons have *positive* charge and neutrons have *no charge*.

TYPES OF RADIATION

The nuclei of some materials are unstable – they have excess energy. These materials are **radioactive** and become stable by emitting α or β particles or γ waves, which can be detected with a Geiger counter or a cloud chamber. The following table summarises their nature and properties.

Type of radiation	Nature	Ability to ionise	Absorption	Effect of magnetic fields
α (alpha)	Helium nucleus, ^4_2He, positive charge	Strong	Absorbed by paper or about 10 cm of air	Small deflection
β (beta)	High energy electron, negative charge	Medium	Absorbed by thin sheets of aluminium	Large deflection
γ (gamma)	High frequency electro-magnetic wave, no charge	Weak	Partly absorbed by thick sheets of lead	No deflection

A radioactive source does not stay alive for ever. The number of active nuclei becomes smaller, and the activity of the source decays in a special way. The *half-life* of a source is the time for the activity to be reduced by a half (*Fig 10.1*).

If 24 grams of radioactive material have a half-life of 2 days, then 12 g will be active after 2 days, 6 g after 4 days, 3 g after 6 days and so on.

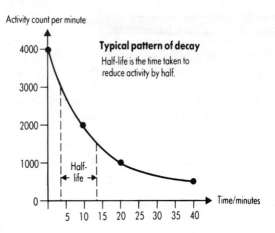

Fig 10.1

NUCLEAR EQUATIONS

When a nucleus decays by emitting an α particle it loses 4 mass units (2 neutrons and 2 protons) and 2 charge units (the protons). It changes into a new material. This can be shown as a *nuclear equation* e.g.

$$\underset{\text{uranium}}{{}^{238}_{92}U} \quad \rightarrow \quad \underset{\text{thorium}}{{}^{234}_{90}Th} \quad + \quad \underset{\text{alpha particle}}{{}^{4}_{2}He}$$

The *upper* number is the **nucleon number** (total number of protons and neutrons) the *lower* number is the **proton number** (total + charge). The general equation for α decay is

$${}^{A}_{Z}X \rightarrow {}^{A-4}_{Z-2}Y + {}^{4}_{2}He$$

In β decay, since negative charge is lost the overall positive charge increases.

$${}^{A}_{Z}X \rightarrow {}^{A}_{Z+1}Y + \quad \uparrow \quad {}^{0}_{-1}e$$
$$\text{(β particle)}$$

γ decay only affects the energy of the nucleus and does not change the chemical nature of the material.

PRACTICE QUESTION

Figure 10.2 illustrates the principle of a roller mill which is used to produce thin metal sheets of constant thickness. The thickness of the metal sheet is checked by using a radioactive source, a Geiger-Müller tube and a scaler.

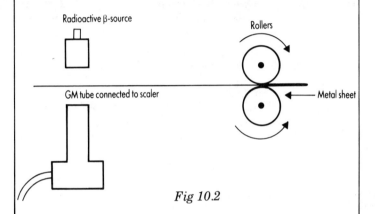

Fig 10.2

a) What would happen to the reading on the detector if for any reason the thickness of the metal sheet passing it decreased?

b) What property of the β source makes it more suitable for this application than an α source?

c) What radioactive source would you employ if the method was adapted to check on a dense metal of several millimetres thickness leaving the rollers?

d) A radioactive source gives off ionising radiation. The workers using radioactive sources must take precautions to avoid exposure to the radiation. Large doses of radiation can damage health.

   i) What precautions should be taken in the use and storage of radioactive sources?

   ii) What are ions?

   iii) Explain the term 'ionising radiation'.

   iv) Explain how exposure to radiation can damage body tissue.   *LEAG (Paper 2)*

Outline Answer

a) The reading would decrease, less β particles would be absorbed.

b) β particles are more penetrating than α particles.

c) A γ source would have to be used since β would be absorbed by this thickness of a dense metal.

d)   *i) Use:*   Handle with tongs.

                  Wear protective clothing with a radiation monitor.

                  Never point a source at the eyes.

        Storage: Store in lead-lined containers.

                  Keep under lock and key in a labelled cupboard.

   ii) An ion is an atom which has lost or gained electrons.

   iii) α, β and γ radiations have high energy. On colliding with an atom they knock electrons out of it, leaving the atom as an ion.

   iv) The danger is due to absorption of energy from the radiation by body tissues. Ions are produced which can change or destroy body cells. Widespread cell damage can kill, and changed body cells can result in cancers.

STUDENT'S ANSWER

with 6examiner's comments 9

a) The reading decreases. ✓

b) Beta particles can pass through the metal but alpha would be absorbed. ✓

c) A gamma source. ✓

d) i) Handle carefully.   'No real detail.'
     Store in a safe place.

   ii) Ions are subatomic particles.   'No. Wrong idea.'

   iii) Radiation that makes ions.   'Not clear.'

   iv) It can cause cancer. ✓

'This answer shows some knowledge but by giving very little detail or explanation it reads poorly.'

TOPIC 11
ELECTRONICS

TRANSISTOR CIRCUITS

Transistor circuits behave like electronic switches. The *base* current controls the transistor and allows a larger *collector* current to flow. There is a *protective resistor* in the base circuit to prevent damage to the transistor (*Fig 11.1*).

The collector current flows if a voltage above 0.7 volts is applied between the base and the 0 volts line. Most transistor circuits depend on a *potential dividing system* (*Fig 11.2*).

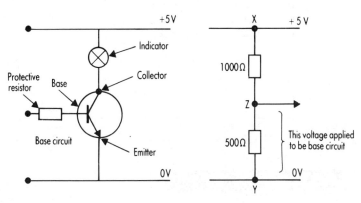

Fig 11.1   *Fig 11.2*

There is always a 5 V potential difference between X and Y. The *potential difference* between Z and Y in this case is

$$\frac{500}{1500} \times 5 = 1.6 \text{ volts}$$

which would 'open' a transistor circuit, allowing a collector current to flow.

HEAT AND LIGHT DEPENDENT RESISTORS

A *heat-dependent resistor* (thermistor) or a *light-dependent resistor* (LDR) both show a drop in resistance if temperature or light intensity increases. They are used in potential divider circuits to act as warning systems. The collector current in transistor circuits is only a few milliamps, so it is often used to operate a *relay* to switch a larger current, for example to operate a motor (*Fig 11.3*).

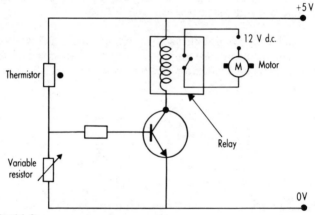

Fig 11.3

LOGIC CIRCUITS

Logic circuits are described by the function they perform. The words NOR, OR, AND, NAND describe the input situation which gives a logic high output.

A *high* input or output is designated logic 1 and *low* is called logic 0 so a circuit described as AND gives an output 1 if both one input AND another are also at logic 1. The functions are usually illustrated with *truth tables*.

PRACTICE QUESTION

An LED is used as an indicator lamp in a temperature-sensing circuit in a small pottery kiln. The LED lights up when the kiln is hot enough to use (see *Fig. 11.4*).

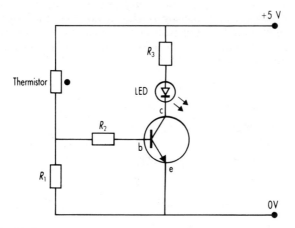

Fig 11.4

i) The circuit is controlled by a thermistor. The resistance of the thermistor decreases as the temperature increases. What happens to the current in the thermistor as the temperature increases?

ii) To switch the transistor ON a voltage of at least 0.6 V is required between the base b and emitter e. At 150°C the p.d. between b and e is 0.3 V. Is the LED alight? Explain your answer.

iii) As the temperature increases the p.d. between b and e increases and the LED lights up. Write several sentences explaining why this happens.

LEAG (Paper 2)

Outline Answer

  i) If the resistance decreases, the current will increase.
 ii) The LED is off. There is not a great enough voltage between b and e to drive the necessary current in the base circuit to open the transistor.
iii) As the temperature rises the thermistor resistance falls. There is always 5 V across the divider circuit, with the greater voltage where there is the larger resistance. Gradually the voltage across the thermistor drops at the same time.

STUDENT'S ANSWER

with ❛examiner's comments❜

i) The current rises. ✓
ii) No.
iii) When the voltage reaches 0.6 V the LED lights.

'Lacking any detail. The question suggests that SEVERAL SENTENCES are needed to explain what happens. They should be written as a careful sequence of events.

INDEX